OWN
YOUR CAREER
OWN YOUR
LIFE

Companion Journal

BY ANDY STORCH

Why you'll love this journal

Here's a few reasons why I think you'll love this journal...

1. This journal will be your guide to your career and life.

2. Help you achieve more by providing a place to record goals and plans as well as track progress and hold you accountable.

3. If you've read my book *Own Your Career Own Your Life*, this journal is designed to be a companion to help reinforce the learning and shift your mindset and behaviors to get more done.

4. Studies show that when you write things down, make commitments and track progress, you are exponentially more likely to achieve your goals.

Own Your Career Own Your Life Journal

Stop Drifting and Take Control of Your Future

Find more resources at
Ownyourcareerownyourlife.com

Table of Contents

Getting Started

This journal is designed to be both a companion to the *Own Your Career Own Your Life* book and also a standalone journal to help you achieve your goals and fulfill your true potential. To take full advantage of this journal, we recommend you:

1. Start by going through the exercises at the beginning of the journal so you can gain clarity on your vision and goals. Refer back to the book whenever possible to get help.

2. Focus on progress over perfection. Nobody is grading you on how you use this journal. Just start and adjust as you go.

3. Make sure you block time every morning and evening to fill in the pages. This will pay off for you over the long run as it will help you achieve more and gain more fulfillment as well.

4. Take this journal with you when you travel and make sure it's always available for you to jot notes and ideas and track progress on your goals.

For more ideas and resources, visit our website:
Ownyourcareerownyourlife.com/journal

You can also ask questions in our free Facebook group:
Ownyourcareerownyourlife.com/Facebook

Let's get started...

"The biggest thing that separates successful people from others is their willingness and ability to take action." -Andy Storch

Before we dig in, let's start with a few questions for you to consider...

First questions:

1. Why did you buy this journal and what do you hope to achieve?

2. What big goals do you currently have?

3. What are the biggest challenges that get in your way?

4. When will you make time to write in this journal?

_____

_____

_____

_____

_____

_____

_____

_____

_____

_____

_____

_____

_____

_____

_____

Habits

Just like in the book *Own Your Career Own Your Life*, you'll notice a habit section on some of the pages. Use this to consider your habits and how you can adjust or establish new healthier habits to achieve your goals.

⊗ **Old Habit:** Drifting through life without setting goals, writing things down or measuring progress

⊘ **New Habit:** Using a journal to write down your vision, goals, thoughts, progress and ideas and taking action daily!

Setting a Vision

Set Your Vision for the Future:

The first step is to set your vision for the future. What do you want to achieve in your career, business and life? Where do you want to go? This is your chance to dream and think big. What would make you happy and fulfilled?

Write down your vision or big goals for the different areas of your life: career, relationships, financial, health, spirituality, intellectual, etc.

There are no wrong answers here. What do you want to achieve or where do you want to be in the next one to five years?

_____

_____

_____

_____

_____

_____

_____

_____

_____

_____

_____

⊗ **Old Habit:** Living life in reaction mode and not ever thinking about where your career is going. Drifting with the wind and blindly doing what you're told

⊘ **New Habit:** Taking time on a weekly or daily basis to think about your career goals, where you want to go, how you want to get there and whether you are making sufficient progress or not. Use this journal to write down ideas, goals and track progress.

Connecting to Purpose

What is your purpose? What is the "why" behind your vision and goals? Why do you want to achieve them? Knowing this will help drive you when things get challenging. Many people skip this step and then give up later when their goals become challenging. You need to know why you are going after these big goals.

Write down your purpose or "why" for each category of your vision you wrote on the previous page. What is driving you? Why do you want to go after these big goals? Only you can decide.

_____

_____

_____

_____

_____

_____

_____

_____

_____

_____

_____

_____

_____

⊗ **Old Habit:** Setting arbitrary goals. Living and working without a clear purpose or "why"

⊘ **New Habit:** Reflecting regularly on your purpose (or "why") and using it as motivation to achieve your vision and big goals. Asking yourself regularly if you feel connected to the work you are doing.

Your Plan (and setting SMART Goals)

They say that a goal without a plan is just a wish. Now that you have set your vision and purpose, do you have a plan? This is a great place to write down all the actions and steps that you think can help you achieve your big vision or goals. It can be helpful to turn them into SMART goals, which means they are specific, measurable, actionable, realistic and time bound.

Finally, write down 1-2 things you can do right away to get you started and then take action.

Once you've written down all your goals and steps, it would be really helpful for you to again share this plan with a friend, colleague and especially your manager (if you're comfortable).

When you share your goals and plans with people you trust and respect, you can get feedback that might help you refine those plans and sett you in the right direction.

What are your goals and what is your plan to achieve them? And what can you do right away?

Goal #1: _____

Plan to achieve it: _____

Action I can take right away: _____

Goal #2: _____

Plan to achieve it: _____

Action I can take right away: _____

Goal #3: _____

Plan to achieve it: _____

Action I can take right away: _____

⊗ **Old Habit:** Operating in reaction mode and setting goals without a plan. Not setting goals that are measurable or time-bound

⊘ **New Habit:** Making a plan and setting SMART goals and milestones and creating habits to support long-term vision and goals.

Who Can Help You?

Humans are social creatures and we are designed to work in groups and help each other. Nobody can do it all on their own so there is no point in trying. If you want to go far in your career and achieve big goals, ask for help in areas where you need it and be sure to seek out opportunities to help others.

Who can help you with your goals? Whom do you need to reach out to? It could be informal help or mentoring or formal coaching/mentoring from someone you hire. Either way it is not only ok but encouraged that you get help achieving your goals. Write own some topics or things you need help with and some people or resources that can help.

_____

_____

_____

_____

_____

_____

_____

_____

_____

_____

_____

_____

> ⊗ **Old Habit:** Trying to do everything yourself and thinking you are weak if you need help
>
> ⊘ **New Habit:** Seeking out and asking for help when you need it and being as helpful as possible to others.

Taking Ownership

To achieve more in your career and be truly fulfilled and content with your life, you've got to take ownership and full responsibility for everything and focus most of your energy on what's in your control and stop wasting time worrying or complaining about things outside of your control. One of the biggest and most important shifts you can make here is to always assume responsibility for everything happening in your life and to avoid a victim mindset. That means no complaining. Nobody likes complainers anyway.

How will you make this shift? Do you need to take more responsibility and complain less? Are you ready to take the "no complaining" challenge and stop complaining for a day, a week, a month or longer? If you are ready to join me in the 30-day "no complaining challenge" and let me and our community know how it goes. Visit ownyourcareerownyourlife.com for more resources.

How will you take more ownership and responsibility in your career and life?

Record your thoughts and plans here:

_____

_____

_____

_____

_____

_____

_____

_____

⊛ **Old Habit:** Placing blame on other people and things. Living with a victim mindset. Believing that life is happening to you and you have no control.

⊙ **New Habit:** Taking full responsibility and ownership for life. Believing life happens FOR you and always finding ways to learn from mistakes. No more complaining!

Continuous Learning

One of the most important things you can do to grow and stay relevant in your field of work, not to mention prepare for future career changes and opportunities, is to invest time in continuous learning. If you are not learning and growing, you might be stagnant or worse. Humans are meant to continue to learn and evolve so never stop learning.

Learning can come from books, articles, podcasts, videos, membership communities, conferences, coaching, masterminds, book clubs and so many other places.

The key is to figure out the resources that will benefit you most and then commit to dedicating time and money on a consistent basis.

Where or how will you invest regularly in your continuous learning and growth?

_____

_____

_____

_____

_____

_____

_____

_____

_____

_____

⊗ **Old Habit:** Spending all your time in reaction mode and never investing time or money into learning and growth

⊘ **New Habit:** Blocking time and investing money on a daily, weekly and monthly basis into learning to help you continue to sharpen your mind and prepare for the future.

Build Your Network

One of the best and most important things you can do to help you prepare for the future of work as well as future career changes and anything else that might come your way is build your network.

This means having meaningful relationships with many different people. The best way to build your network is to show up (personally or virtually), be curious, ask questions, seek to help others and give as much value as you can to those around you.

If you are helping or giving enough value to others, it will almost always come back to you.

You can build your network by attending conferences, networking events, talking with people in your office or company, going on LinkedIn or other social platforms.

Where and how will you build your network over the next 90 days? What networking habits will you establish? How often will you connect with new people? Declare it and write it down!

_____

_____

_____

_____

_____

_____

_____

_____

> ⊛ **Old Habit:** Not making time for networking. Putting it off for someday and focusing only on the work in front of you.
>
> ⊘ **New Habit:** Investing time and money regularly into networking. Decide how much you can dedicate and start spending or investing money into networking on a regular basis and see how it starts to pay off for your life and career.

Build Your Personal or Professional Brand

Your personal or professional brand is basically your reputation. It's what people think about you or say about you when you're not around. And you obviously want that reputation to be positive and to help you in your career.

Building your personal brand means being intentional about building a positive reputation (while staying authentic and true to yourself). Those with strong brands are more likely to get promoted or that next great project, not to mention a better job in the future. So you need to spend time building your brand.

How and where you build your brand can include how you show up at the office, the projects you take on, the work you do, the way you interact with colleagues and of course how you show up online and on social media as well. The best place to build a brand in the professional or corporate space is on LinkedIn. You can do this by connecting with people, commenting on posts and sharing your own content.

Content can include articles or books you've read, goals you're setting, and your own thoughts and opinions on things shared via articles, videos, short and long form posts. It's up to you.

So how will you build your personal brand or reputation?

_____

_____

_____

_____

_____

_____

⊗ **Old Habit:** Paying no attention to your brand or reputation. Avoiding social media or only consuming content and never sharing your own.

⊘ **New Habit:** Being intentional about how you show up and the projects you take at work. Spending more intentional time on LinkedIn or other social media channels. Leaving thoughtful comments on posts and sharing more of your own content on a regular basis.

Mindset

Your mindset, how you approach life and how you perceive the world is so critical to your success and happiness. If you read Own Your Career Own Your Life, you know what it means to have a "growth mindset" and how important it is to approach life with the attitude that we can learn from every situation and we can always improve. Mindset is everything.

With an attitude of ownership and a growth mindset, you know there is no way to fail. Instead we know we can grow and learn from every situation. We also know that major achievement, success and fulfillment often comes from overcoming challenges and getting outside of our comfort zones.

What often gets in your way? What can you do to improve or shift your mindset and how will you get out of your comfort zone to challenge yourself and try new things in the next 90 days?

Write your thoughts below:

_____

_____

_____

_____

_____

_____

_____

_____

(✷) **Old Habit:** Avoiding risks, fearing failure or rejection, never trying new things, believing that you are a victim or life happens to you.

(✓) **New Habit:** Embracing change and risk, trying new things, and getting outside of your comfort zone on a regular basis to learn and grow and taking full responsibility for everything in your life.

Self-Awareness

Self-awareness is a critical factor for leadership and success. The more aware you are of how you show up in the world – your strengths, weaknesses, attitude, personality, mindset and how you affect other people – the more you can learn, adjust and take big action to grow your career and life.

It's important to be aware of how you show up in the world. What are your strengths? What are some weaknesses you have, and do you want to work on improving them or just simply avoid them? How or where is your personality an asset and where does it maybe cause challenges or hold you back?

For example, if you are an extroverted, relational, adventurous person like me, you may get energy and excel in doing work involving other people but may struggle with quiet, detail-oriented work. It's important to be aware of these things.

Write down some thoughts about who you are and how you show up in the world. And what else can you do to improve your self-awareness? Who can give you feedback about strengths and potential blind spots?

_____

_____

_____

_____

_____

_____

_____

> ⊗ **Old Habit:** Operating with no self-awareness and not ever considering your reputation or how you show up in the world. Avoiding feedback.
>
> ⊘ **New Habit:** Thinking regularly about how to leverage your strengths, how to improve or delegate your weaknesses and how you show up in the workplace and how that impacts your reputation.

Prioritizing Time

Everyone on this planet has the same amount of time in a day and a week. But most people don't use that time productively. Instead they waste time doing things that don't help them improve their lives or achieve their goals. How you choose to prioritize your time will have a big impact on your ability to achieve your goals.

In this section, reflect on how you have been prioritizing your time and how you can improve. What do you do on a weekly basis that is not productive? What do you need to start doing or do more of? For example, if your goal is to build a bigger network, you may need to start going to more networking events and spend at least two hours per week on LinkedIn.

How you spend your time is up to you but you need to be intentional and honest with yourself. You have time to do anything you want.

Are you spending your time in the best places to help you achieve your goals? How can you adjust your schedule and the way you spend your time to help you achieve your goals? Can you be more honest about how much time you have? Can you be more thoughtful about how you spend your time?

Write your thoughts here:

_____

_____

_____

_____

_____

_____

> ⊛ **Old Habit:** Drifting along, lying to yourself (and others), making excuses, letting others control your time and schedule and procrastinating on the things you know you need or want to do.
>
> ⊘ **New Habit:** Taking ownership and responsibility, being honest about how much time you have and how you choose to use it, scheduling time to do the most important things and spending less time on passive, unimportant activities.

Accountability

Having accountability from others is one of the biggest things you can do to help accelerate your chances of achieving your goals. To gain more accountability you can hire a coach, join a mastermind group, find an accountability buddy (a friend working on a similar goal), talk to your manager or start a spreadsheet and track your actions and hold yourself accountable.

All of these things work but you have to be willing to write your goals down, share them with others and ask them to hold you accountable.

Who can help hold you accountable to your goals? Where can you share your goals to gain more accountability?

> (✖) **Old Habit:** Keeping your goals a secret so that nobody will know if you fail.
>
> (✓) **New Habit:** Telling other people about your goals, hiring a coach or finding people to hold you accountable so you are more likely to achieve your goals.

Habits

Another critical factor that can help you achieve big goals and take control of your future is establishing healthy habits that support your goals. Some healthy habits could include: a strict morning routine, reading each day, writing in a journal, meditation, exercise, regular networking, posting on social media, helping colleagues, doing scary things, etc.

When I decided to write my book and create this journal, I set a habit to write 500 words per day and work on the book and journal every morning before other work. That helped me make progress on a daily basis.

What healthy habits do you need to establish to help you achieve your goals and take control of your future? What other habits do you need to eliminate?

_____

_____

_____

_____

_____

_____

_____

_____

_____

_____

_____

_____

> (✷) **Old Habit:** Setting big goals but not breaking them down into habits. Drifting along without thinking about how every action can help or hinder progress.
>
> (✓) **New Habit:** Breaking goals down into daily or weekly habits that help make consistent progress toward achieving a goal or vision.

Tracking Progress and Using this Journal

Now that we have established our big goals, our plans, where we can get help and accountability, shifted our mindset, prioritized our time found accountability and established our habits, it's time to start tracking progress.

They say that "what gets measured, gets done." If you are working on big goals and taking ownership of your career and future, you need to measure progress. That's why I created this journal. You can use the rest of this journal to record and track your gratitude, achievements, progress and frustrations so that you can see the progress you are making and achieve more.

Some notes:

Gratitude – Studies show that practicing gratitude on a daily basis will make you happier and more fulfilled. We have already committed to taking ownership, which means no more victim mindset or complaining. You can enhance that future by practicing gratitude on a daily basis. This simply means taking a few moments to reflect on the things you are grateful for. These could be as important as a spouse, kids or family or as trivial as a quiet house and warm cup of coffee. As I write this, I am grateful for the ability to write, the opportunity to serve you and I am very grateful that you are using this journal.

You will see a spot for gratitude every morning and I recommend you don't skip it. This practice alone can change your life.

Your vision or big goal – it can be helpful to remind yourself of your vision or big goal you are working on or towards. Many successful people recommend writing it down and reciting it daily. You can also add this to your daily affirmations. For example as I was working on my book and this journal, I wrote down daily in my journal that my big goal was to publish a book and journal by the end of the year.

Planning your day – Some people have very consistent schedules and therefore this may not be as useful, but for people like me who have a lot of things going it, it can be very helpful to write down your schedule and the big things you want to achieve throughout the day and week. Use this accordingly. I recommend you spend time every morning planning your day and every evening reflecting on what worked and what didn't.

Reflecting on the day – you'll notice that each day has a morning section and evening section. This is so you can use your journal to open and plan your day as well as close the day out by reflecting on what you achieved and did not achieve as well as what you want to get done tomorrow. Don't skip this. Measuring progress and reflecting on what you achieved and what's working and not working is very helpful.

Are you ready?

Day 1 Morning Ritual | Date: _____

 All our dreams can come true, if we have the courage to pursue them. – Walt Disney

I am grateful for...

_____

_____

_____

My big vision or goal I'm working toward:

_____

_____

_____

The thing(s) I will accomplish today to support my vision and goals:

1. _____

2. _____

3. _____

My schedule or action plan:

_____

_____

_____

_____

Thoughts/ideas:

_____

_____

_____

_____

Day 1 Evening Ritual

What great things happened today? What did you get done?

_____

_____

_____

_____

What could've gone better? What lessons did you learn?

_____

_____

_____

_____

What do you want to accomplish tomorrow?

_____

_____

_____

_____

Final notes and ideas:

_____

_____

_____

_____

Day 2 Morning Ritual | Date: _____

 The secret of getting ahead is
getting started. – Mark Twain

I am grateful for...

_____

_____

My big vision or goal I'm working toward:

_____

_____

The thing(s) I will accomplish today to support my vision and goals:

1. _____

2. _____

3. _____

My schedule or action plan:

_____

_____

_____

Thoughts/ideas:

_____

_____

_____

Day 2 Evening Ritual

What great things happened today? What did you get done?

_____

_____

_____

_____

What could've gone better? What lessons did you learn?

_____

_____

_____

_____

What do you want to accomplish tomorrow?

_____

_____

_____

_____

Final notes and ideas:

_____

_____

_____

_____

Day 3 Morning Ritual | Date: _____

> **"** I've missed more than 9,000 shots in my career. I've lost almost 300 games. 26 times I've been trusted to take the game winning shot and missed. I've failed over and over and over again in my life and that is why I succeed. – Michael Jordan **"**

I am grateful for...

_____
_____
_____

My big vision or goal I'm working toward:

_____
_____
_____

The thing(s) I will accomplish today to support my vision and goals:

1. _____

2. _____

3. _____

My schedule or action plan:

_____
_____
_____
_____

Thoughts/ideas:

_____
_____

Day 3 Evening Ritual

What great things happened today? What did you get done?

_____

_____

_____

_____

What could've gone better? What lessons did you learn?

_____

_____

_____

_____

What do you want to accomplish tomorrow?

_____

_____

_____

_____

Final notes and ideas:

_____

_____

_____

_____

Day 4 Morning Ritual | Date: _____

> " Don't limit yourself. Many people limit themselves to what they think they can do. You can go as far as your mind lets you. What you believe, remember, you can achieve. – Mary Kay Ash "

I am grateful for...

_____

_____

_____

My big vision or goal I'm working toward:

_____

_____

_____

The thing(s) I will accomplish today to support my vision and goals:

1. _____

2. _____

3. _____

My schedule or action plan:

_____

_____

_____

_____

Thoughts/ideas:

_____

_____

_____

Day 4 Evening Ritual

What great things happened today? What did you get done?

_____

_____

_____

_____

What could've gone better? What lessons did you learn?

_____

_____

_____

_____

What do you want to accomplish tomorrow?

_____

_____

_____

_____

Final notes and ideas:

_____

_____

_____

_____

Day 5 Morning Ritual | Date: _____

 The best time to plant a tree was 20 years ago.
The second best time is now. – Chinese Proverb

I am grateful for...

_____

_____

_____

My big vision or goal I'm working toward:

_____

_____

The thing(s) I will accomplish today to support my vision and goals:

1. _____

2. _____

3. _____

My schedule or action plan:

_____

_____

_____

Thoughts/ideas:

_____

_____

_____

Day 5 Evening Ritual

What great things happened today? What did you get done?

_____

_____

_____

_____

What could've gone better? What lessons did you learn?

_____

_____

_____

_____

What do you want to accomplish tomorrow?

_____

_____

_____

_____

Final notes and ideas:

_____

_____

_____

_____

Day 6 Morning Ritual | Date: _____

I am grateful for...

_____

_____

_____

My big vision or goal I'm working toward:

_____

_____

_____

The thing(s) I will accomplish today to support my vision and goals:

1. _____

2. _____

3. _____

My schedule or action plan:

_____

_____

_____

_____

Thoughts/ideas:

_____

_____

_____

_____

Day 6 Evening Ritual

What great things happened today? What did you get done?

_____

_____

_____

_____

What could've gone better? What lessons did you learn?

_____

_____

_____

_____

What do you want to accomplish tomorrow?

_____

_____

_____

_____

Final notes and ideas:

_____

_____

_____

_____

Day 7 Morning Ritual | Date: _____

> Do one thing every day that scares you.
> – Eleanor Roosevelt

I am grateful for...

_____

_____

_____

My big vision or goal I'm working toward:

_____

_____

_____

The thing(s) I will accomplish today to support my vision and goals:

1. _____

2. _____

3. _____

My schedule or action plan:

_____

_____

_____

_____

Thoughts/ideas:

_____

_____

_____

_____

Day 7 Evening Ritual

What great things happened today? What did you get done?

_____

_____

_____

_____

What could've gone better? What lessons did you learn?

_____

_____

_____

_____

What do you want to accomplish tomorrow?

_____

_____

_____

_____

Final notes and ideas:

_____

_____

_____

_____

Day 8 Morning Ritual | Date: _____

 It's no use going back to yesterday, because I was a different person then. – Lewis Carroll

I am grateful for...

_____

_____

_____

My big vision or goal I'm working toward:

_____

_____

The thing(s) I will accomplish today to support my vision and goals:

1. _____

2. _____

3. _____

My schedule or action plan:

_____

_____

_____

Thoughts/ideas:

_____

_____

 _____

_____

Day 8 Evening Ritual

What great things happened today? What did you get done?

_____

_____

_____

_____

What could've gone better? What lessons did you learn?

_____

_____

_____

_____

What do you want to accomplish tomorrow?

_____

_____

_____

_____

Final notes and ideas:

_____

_____

_____

_____

Day 9 Morning Ritual | Date: _____

> Smart people learn from everything and everyone, average people from their experiences, stupid people already have all the answers. – Socrates

I am grateful for...

_____

_____

_____

My big vision or goal I'm working toward:

_____

_____

The thing(s) I will accomplish today to support my vision and goals:

1. _____

2. _____

3. _____

My schedule or action plan:

_____

_____

_____

Thoughts/ideas:

_____

_____

_____

Day 9 Evening Ritual

What great things happened today? What did you get done?

_____

_____

_____

_____

What could've gone better? What lessons did you learn?

_____

_____

_____

_____

What do you want to accomplish tomorrow?

_____

_____

_____

_____

Final notes and ideas:

_____

_____

_____

_____

_____

Day 10 Morning Ritual | Date: _____

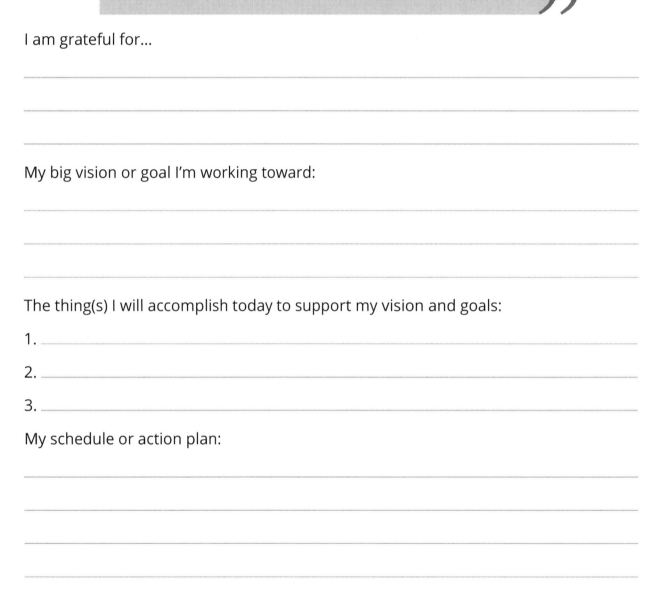

> " Do what you feel in your heart to be right – for you'll be criticized anyway. – Eleanor Roosevelt "

I am grateful for...

_____

_____

_____

My big vision or goal I'm working toward:

_____

_____

_____

The thing(s) I will accomplish today to support my vision and goals:

1. _____

2. _____

3. _____

My schedule or action plan:

_____

_____

_____

Thoughts/ideas:

_____

_____

_____

Day 10 Evening Ritual

What great things happened today? What did you get done?

What could've gone better? What lessons did you learn?

What do you want to accomplish tomorrow?

Final notes and ideas:

Day 11 Morning Ritual | Date: _____

> "Happiness is not something ready made. It comes from your own actions." – Dalai Lama XIV

I am grateful for...

_____

_____

_____

My big vision or goal I'm working toward:

_____

_____

_____

The thing(s) I will accomplish today to support my vision and goals:

1. _____

2. _____

3. _____

My schedule or action plan:

_____

_____

_____

Thoughts/ideas:

_____

_____

_____

Day 11 Evening Ritual

What great things happened today? What did you get done?

_____

_____

_____

_____

What could've gone better? What lessons did you learn?

_____

_____

_____

_____

_____

What do you want to accomplish tomorrow?

_____

_____

_____

_____

Final notes and ideas:

_____

_____

_____

_____

_____

Day 12 Morning Ritual | Date: _____

 If we have the attitude that it's going to be a great day it usually is. – Catherine Pulsifier

I am grateful for...

_____

_____

_____

My big vision or goal I'm working toward:

_____

_____

_____

The thing(s) I will accomplish today to support my vision and goals:

1. _____

2. _____

3. _____

My schedule or action plan:

_____

_____

_____

_____

Thoughts/ideas:

_____

_____

_____

_____

Day 12 Evening Ritual

What great things happened today? What did you get done?

_____

_____

_____

_____

What could've gone better? What lessons did you learn?

_____

_____

_____

_____

What do you want to accomplish tomorrow?

_____

_____

_____

_____

Final notes and ideas:

_____

_____

_____

_____

Day 13 Morning Ritual | Date: _____

> You can either experience the pain of discipline or the pain of regret. The choice is yours. – Unknown

I am grateful for...

_____
_____
_____

My big vision or goal I'm working toward:

_____
_____
_____

The thing(s) I will accomplish today to support my vision and goals:

1. _____

2. _____

3. _____

My schedule or action plan:

_____
_____
_____
_____

Thoughts/ideas:

_____
_____
_____

Day 13 Evening Ritual

What great things happened today? What did you get done?

_____

_____

_____

_____

What could've gone better? What lessons did you learn?

_____

_____

_____

_____

What do you want to accomplish tomorrow?

_____

_____

_____

_____

Final notes and ideas:

_____

_____

_____

_____

_____

Day 14 Morning Ritual | Date: _____

> Impossible is just an opinion.
> – Paulo Coelho

I am grateful for...

_____
_____

_____

My big vision or goal I'm working toward:

_____

_____

_____

The thing(s) I will accomplish today to support my vision and goals:

1. _____

2. _____

3. _____

My schedule or action plan:

_____

_____

_____

Thoughts/ideas:

_____

_____

_____

Day 14 Evening Ritual

What great things happened today? What did you get done?

_____

_____

_____

_____

What could've gone better? What lessons did you learn?

_____

_____

_____

_____

What do you want to accomplish tomorrow?

_____

_____

_____

_____

Final notes and ideas:

_____

_____

_____

_____

Day 15 Morning Ritual | Date: _____

 Your passion is waiting for your courage
to catch up. – Isabelle Lafleche

I am grateful for...

_____

_____

_____

My big vision or goal I'm working toward:

_____

_____

_____

The thing(s) I will accomplish today to support my vision and goals:

1. _____

2. _____

3. _____

My schedule or action plan:

_____

_____

_____

Thoughts/ideas:

_____

_____

_____

Day 15 Evening Ritual

What great things happened today? What did you get done?

_____

_____

_____

_____

What could've gone better? What lessons did you learn?

_____

_____

_____

_____

What do you want to accomplish tomorrow?

_____

_____

_____

_____

Final notes and ideas:

_____

_____

_____

_____

Day 16 Morning Ritual | Date: _____

> Magic is believing in yourself. If you can make that happen, you can make anything happen.
> – Johann Wolfgang Von Goethe

I am grateful for...

_____

_____

_____

My big vision or goal I'm working toward:

_____

_____

_____

The thing(s) I will accomplish today to support my vision and goals:

1. _____

2. _____

3. _____

My schedule or action plan:

_____

_____

_____

_____

Thoughts/ideas:

_____

_____

_____

_____

Day 16 Evening Ritual

What great things happened today? What did you get done?

What could've gone better? What lessons did you learn?

What do you want to accomplish tomorrow?

Final notes and ideas:

Day 17 Morning Ritual | Date: _____

> If something is important enough, even if the odds are stacked against you, you should still do it. – Elon Musk

I am grateful for...

_____
_____
_____

My big vision or goal I'm working toward:

_____
_____
_____

The thing(s) I will accomplish today to support my vision and goals:

1. _____

2. _____

3. _____

My schedule or action plan:

_____
_____
_____
_____

Thoughts/ideas:

_____
_____
_____

Day 17 Evening Ritual

What great things happened today? What did you get done?

_____

_____

_____

_____

What could've gone better? What lessons did you learn?

_____

_____

_____

_____

What do you want to accomplish tomorrow?

_____

_____

_____

_____

Final notes and ideas:

_____

_____

_____

_____

_____

Day 18 Morning Ritual | Date: _____

> **There is nothing to fear, because you cannot fail—only learn, grow, and become better than you've ever been before. – Hal Elrod**

I am grateful for...

_____

_____

_____

My big vision or goal I'm working toward:

_____

_____

The thing(s) I will accomplish today to support my vision and goals:

1. _____

2. _____

3. _____

My schedule or action plan:

_____

_____

_____

Thoughts/ideas:

_____

_____

_____

Day 18 Evening Ritual

What great things happened today? What did you get done?

What could've gone better? What lessons did you learn?

What do you want to accomplish tomorrow?

Final notes and ideas:

Day 19 Morning Ritual | Date: _____

> Don't be afraid to give up the good to go for the great. – John D. Rockefeller

I am grateful for...

_____

_____

_____

My big vision or goal I'm working toward:

_____

_____

_____

The thing(s) I will accomplish today to support my vision and goals:

1. _____

2. _____

3. _____

My schedule or action plan:

_____

_____

_____

_____

Thoughts/ideas:

_____

_____

_____

Day 19 Evening Ritual

What great things happened today? What did you get done?

_____

_____

_____

_____

What could've gone better? What lessons did you learn?

_____

_____

_____

_____

What do you want to accomplish tomorrow?

_____

_____

_____

_____

Final notes and ideas:

_____

_____

_____

_____

Day 20 Morning Ritual | Date: _____

 Things may come to those who wait, but only the things left by those who hustle. – Abraham Lincoln

I am grateful for...

_____

_____

My big vision or goal I'm working toward:

_____

_____

The thing(s) I will accomplish today to support my vision and goals:

1. _____

2. _____

3. _____

My schedule or action plan:

_____

_____

_____

Thoughts/ideas:

_____

_____

 _____

Day 20 Evening Ritual

What great things happened today? What did you get done?

_____

_____

_____

_____

What could've gone better? What lessons did you learn?

_____

_____

_____

_____

What do you want to accomplish tomorrow?

_____

_____

_____

_____

Final notes and ideas:

_____

_____

_____

_____

Day 21 Morning Ritual | Date: _____

> Without hustle, talent will only carry you so far. – Gary Vaynerchuk

I am grateful for...

_____
_____
_____

My big vision or goal I'm working toward:

_____
_____
_____

The thing(s) I will accomplish today to support my vision and goals:

1. _____

2. _____

3. _____

My schedule or action plan:

_____
_____
_____
_____

Thoughts/ideas:

_____
_____
_____

Day 21 Evening Ritual

What great things happened today? What did you get done?

_____

_____

_____

_____

What could've gone better? What lessons did you learn?

_____

_____

_____

_____

What do you want to accomplish tomorrow?

_____

_____

_____

_____

Final notes and ideas:

_____

_____

_____

_____

Day 22 Morning Ritual | Date: _____

> Work like there is someone working twenty four hours a day to take it away from you. – Mark Cuban

I am grateful for...

_____

_____

My big vision or goal I'm working toward:

_____

_____

The thing(s) I will accomplish today to support my vision and goals:

1. _____

2. _____

3. _____

My schedule or action plan:

_____

_____

_____

Thoughts/ideas:

_____

_____

_____

Day 22 Evening Ritual

What great things happened today? What did you get done?

_____

_____

_____

_____

What could've gone better? What lessons did you learn?

_____

_____

_____

_____

What do you want to accomplish tomorrow?

_____

_____

_____

_____

Final notes and ideas:

_____

_____

_____

_____

Day 23 Morning Ritual | Date: _____

 We are what we repeatedly do. Excellence, then, is not an act, but a habit. – Aristotle

I am grateful for...

_____

_____

_____

My big vision or goal I'm working toward:

_____

_____

_____

The thing(s) I will accomplish today to support my vision and goals:

1. _____

2. _____

3. _____

My schedule or action plan:

_____

_____

_____

_____

Thoughts/ideas:

_____

_____

_____

_____

Day 23 Evening Ritual

What great things happened today? What did you get done?

_____

_____

_____

_____

What could've gone better? What lessons did you learn?

_____

_____

_____

_____

What do you want to accomplish tomorrow?

_____

_____

_____

_____

Final notes and ideas:

_____

_____

_____

_____

Day 24 Morning Ritual | Date: _____

 If you're offered a seat on a rocket ship, don't ask what seat! Just get on. – Sheryl Sandberg

I am grateful for...

_____

_____

_____

My big vision or goal I'm working toward:

_____

_____

_____

The thing(s) I will accomplish today to support my vision and goals:

1. _____

2. _____

3. _____

My schedule or action plan:

_____

_____

_____

_____

Thoughts/ideas:

_____

_____

_____

_____

Day 24 Evening Ritual

What great things happened today? What did you get done?

_____

_____

_____

_____

What could've gone better? What lessons did you learn?

_____

_____

_____

_____

What do you want to accomplish tomorrow?

_____

_____

_____

_____

Final notes and ideas:

_____

_____

_____

_____

Day 25 Morning Ritual | Date: _____

 I always did something I was a little not ready to do. I think that's how you grow. – Marissa Mayer

I am grateful for...

_____

_____

_____

My big vision or goal I'm working toward:

_____

_____

_____

The thing(s) I will accomplish today to support my vision and goals:

1. _____

2. _____

3. _____

My schedule or action plan:

_____

_____

_____

_____

Thoughts/ideas:

_____

_____

_____

Day 25 Evening Ritual

What great things happened today? What did you get done?

_____

_____

_____

_____

What could've gone better? What lessons did you learn?

_____

_____

_____

_____

What do you want to accomplish tomorrow?

_____

_____

_____

_____

Final notes and ideas:

_____

_____

_____

_____

Day 26 Morning Ritual | Date: _____

> If you hear a voice within you say 'you cannot paint,' then by all means paint and that voice will be silenced. – Vincent Van Gogh

I am grateful for...

_____
_____
_____

My big vision or goal I'm working toward:

_____
_____
_____

The thing(s) I will accomplish today to support my vision and goals:

1. _____
2. _____
3. _____

My schedule or action plan:

_____
_____
_____
_____

Thoughts/ideas:

_____
_____
_____

Day 26 Evening Ritual

What great things happened today? What did you get done?

What could've gone better? What lessons did you learn?

What do you want to accomplish tomorrow?

Final notes and ideas:

Day 27 Morning Ritual | Date: _____

 How wonderful it is that nobody need wait a single moment before starting to improve the world. – Anne Frank

I am grateful for...

_____

_____

_____

My big vision or goal I'm working toward:

_____

_____

_____

The thing(s) I will accomplish today to support my vision and goals:

1. _____

2. _____

3. _____

My schedule or action plan:

_____

_____

_____

_____

Thoughts/ideas:

_____

_____

_____

_____

Day 27 Evening Ritual

What great things happened today? What did you get done?

_____

_____

_____

_____

What could've gone better? What lessons did you learn?

_____

_____

_____

_____

What do you want to accomplish tomorrow?

_____

_____

_____

_____

Final notes and ideas:

_____

_____

_____

_____

Day 28 Morning Ritual | Date: _____

 Some people want it to happen, some wish it would happen, others make it happen. – Michael Jordan

I am grateful for...

_____

_____

_____

My big vision or goal I'm working toward:

_____

_____

The thing(s) I will accomplish today to support my vision and goals:

1. _____

2. _____

3. _____

My schedule or action plan:

_____

_____

_____

Thoughts/ideas:

_____

_____

_____

Day 28 Evening Ritual

What great things happened today? What did you get done?

_____

_____

_____

_____

What could've gone better? What lessons did you learn?

_____

_____

_____

_____

What do you want to accomplish tomorrow?

_____

_____

_____

_____

Final notes and ideas:

_____

_____

_____

_____

Day 29 Morning Ritual | Date: _____

 Great things are done by a series of small things brought together – Vincent Van Gogh

I am grateful for...

_____
_____
_____

My big vision or goal I'm working toward:

_____
_____

The thing(s) I will accomplish today to support my vision and goals:

1. _____

2. _____

3. _____

My schedule or action plan:

_____
_____
_____

Thoughts/ideas:

_____
_____
_____
_____

Day 29 Evening Ritual

What great things happened today? What did you get done?

What could've gone better? What lessons did you learn?

What do you want to accomplish tomorrow?

Final notes and ideas:

Day 30 Morning Ritual | Date: _____

> Very often, a change of self is needed
> more than a change of scene. – A.C. Benson

I am grateful for...

_____

_____

_____

My big vision or goal I'm working toward:

_____

_____

_____

The thing(s) I will accomplish today to support my vision and goals:

1. _____

2. _____

3. _____

My schedule or action plan:

_____

_____

_____

_____

Thoughts/ideas:

_____

_____

_____

Day 30 Evening Ritual

What great things happened today? What did you get done?

_____

_____

_____

_____

What could've gone better? What lessons did you learn?

_____

_____

_____

_____

What do you want to accomplish tomorrow?

_____

_____

_____

_____

Final notes and ideas:

_____

_____

_____

_____

Day 31 Morning Ritual | Date: _____

> The hard days are what make you stronger.
> – Aly Raisman

I am grateful for...

_____

_____

_____

My big vision or goal I'm working toward:

_____

_____

_____

The thing(s) I will accomplish today to support my vision and goals:

1. _____

2. _____

3. _____

My schedule or action plan:

_____

_____

_____

_____

Thoughts/ideas:

_____

_____

_____

Day 31 Evening Ritual

What great things happened today? What did you get done?

What could've gone better? What lessons did you learn?

What do you want to accomplish tomorrow?

Final notes and ideas:

Day 32 Morning Ritual | Date: _____

> " If you believe it'll work out, you'll see opportunities. If you don't believe it'll work out, you'll see obstacles. – Wayne Dyer "

I am grateful for...

_____

_____

_____

My big vision or goal I'm working toward:

_____

_____

_____

The thing(s) I will accomplish today to support my vision and goals:

1. _____

2. _____

3. _____

My schedule or action plan:

_____

_____

_____

Thoughts/ideas:

_____

_____

_____

Day 32 Evening Ritual

What great things happened today? What did you get done?

What could've gone better? What lessons did you learn?

What do you want to accomplish tomorrow?

Final notes and ideas:

Day 33 Morning Ritual | Date: _____

> Keep your eyes on the stars, and your feet on the ground. – Theodore Roosevelt

I am grateful for...

_____

_____

_____

My big vision or goal I'm working toward:

_____

_____

_____

The thing(s) I will accomplish today to support my vision and goals:

1. _____

2. _____

3. _____

My schedule or action plan:

_____

_____

_____

_____

Thoughts/ideas:

_____

_____

_____

_____

Day 33 Evening Ritual

What great things happened today? What did you get done?

_____

_____

_____

_____

What could've gone better? What lessons did you learn?

_____

_____

_____

_____

What do you want to accomplish tomorrow?

_____

_____

_____

_____

Final notes and ideas:

_____

_____

_____

_____

Day 34 Morning Ritual | Date: _____

> ❝ You've got to get up every morning with determination if you're going to go to bed with satisfaction. – George Lorimer ❞

I am grateful for...

_____

_____

_____

My big vision or goal I'm working toward:

_____

_____

The thing(s) I will accomplish today to support my vision and goals:

1. _____

2. _____

3. _____

My schedule or action plan:

_____

_____

_____

Thoughts/ideas:

_____

_____

_____

Day 34 Evening Ritual

What great things happened today? What did you get done?

_____

_____

_____

_____

What could've gone better? What lessons did you learn?

_____

_____

_____

_____

What do you want to accomplish tomorrow?

_____

_____

_____

_____

Final notes and ideas:

_____

_____

_____

_____

Day 35 Morning Ritual | Date: _____

> Hard work beats talent when talent doesn't work hard. – Tim Notke

I am grateful for...

_____

_____

_____

My big vision or goal I'm working toward:

_____

_____

The thing(s) I will accomplish today to support my vision and goals:

1. _____

2. _____

3. _____

My schedule or action plan:

_____

_____

_____

Thoughts/ideas:

_____

_____

_____

Day 35 Evening Ritual

What great things happened today? What did you get done?

_____

_____

_____

_____

What could've gone better? What lessons did you learn?

_____

_____

_____

_____

What do you want to accomplish tomorrow?

_____

_____

_____

_____

Final notes and ideas:

_____

_____

_____

_____

_____

Day 36 Morning Ritual | Date: _____

 If everything seems to be under control, you're not going fast enough. – Mario Andretti

I am grateful for...

_____
_____
_____

My big vision or goal I'm working toward:

_____
_____
_____

The thing(s) I will accomplish today to support my vision and goals:

1. _____
2. _____
3. _____

My schedule or action plan:

_____
_____
_____
_____

Thoughts/ideas:

_____
_____
_____

Day 36 Evening Ritual

What great things happened today? What did you get done?

_____

_____

_____

_____

What could've gone better? What lessons did you learn?

_____

_____

_____

_____

What do you want to accomplish tomorrow?

_____

_____

_____

_____

Final notes and ideas:

_____

_____

_____

_____

_____

Day 37 Morning Ritual | Date: _____

 Opportunity is missed by most people because it is dressed in overalls and looks like work. – Thomas Edison

I am grateful for...

_____

_____

_____

My big vision or goal I'm working toward:

_____

_____

The thing(s) I will accomplish today to support my vision and goals:

1. _____

2. _____

3. _____

My schedule or action plan:

_____

_____

_____

Thoughts/ideas:

_____

_____

 _____

_____

Day 37 Evening Ritual

What great things happened today? What did you get done?

_____

_____

_____

_____

What could've gone better? What lessons did you learn?

_____

_____

_____

_____

What do you want to accomplish tomorrow?

_____

_____

_____

_____

Final notes and ideas:

_____

_____

_____

_____

Day 38 Morning Ritual | Date: _____

> The only difference between ordinary and extraordinary is that little extra. – Jimmy Johnson

I am grateful for...

_____

_____

_____

My big vision or goal I'm working toward:

_____

_____

_____

The thing(s) I will accomplish today to support my vision and goals:

1. _____

2. _____

3. _____

My schedule or action plan:

_____

_____

_____

_____

Thoughts/ideas:

_____

_____

_____

_____

Day 38 Evening Ritual

What great things happened today? What did you get done?

What could've gone better? What lessons did you learn?

What do you want to accomplish tomorrow?

Final notes and ideas:

Day 39 Morning Ritual | Date: _____

> Unsuccessful people make their decisions based on their current situations. Successful people make their decisions based on where they want to be. – Benjamin Hardy

I am grateful for...

_____

_____

_____

My big vision or goal I'm working toward:

_____

_____

_____

The thing(s) I will accomplish today to support my vision and goals:

1. _____

2. _____

3. _____

My schedule or action plan:

_____

_____

_____

_____

Thoughts/ideas:

_____

_____

_____

Day 39 Evening Ritual

What great things happened today? What did you get done?

_____

_____

_____

_____

What could've gone better? What lessons did you learn?

_____

_____

_____

_____

What do you want to accomplish tomorrow?

_____

_____

_____

_____

Final notes and ideas:

_____

_____

_____

_____

_____

Day 40 Morning Ritual | Date: _____

> Never stop doing your best just because someone
> doesn't give you credit. – Kamari aka Lyrikal

I am grateful for...

_____

_____

_____

My big vision or goal I'm working toward:

_____

_____

The thing(s) I will accomplish today to support my vision and goals:

1. _____

2. _____

3. _____

My schedule or action plan:

_____

_____

_____

Thoughts/ideas:

_____

_____

_____

Day 40 Evening Ritual

What great things happened today? What did you get done?

What could've gone better? What lessons did you learn?

What do you want to accomplish tomorrow?

Final notes and ideas:

Day 41 Morning Ritual | Date: _____

 Work hard, be kind, and amazing things will happen. - Conan O'Brien

I am grateful for...

_____

_____

_____

My big vision or goal I'm working toward:

_____

_____

_____

The thing(s) I will accomplish today to support my vision and goals:

1. _____

2. _____

3. _____

My schedule or action plan:

_____

_____

_____

Thoughts/ideas:

_____

_____

_____

Day 41 Evening Ritual

What great things happened today? What did you get done?

What could've gone better? What lessons did you learn?

What do you want to accomplish tomorrow?

Final notes and ideas:

Day 42 Morning Ritual | Date: _____

> " Never give up on a dream just because of the time
> it will take to accomplish it. The time will pass anyway.
> – Earl Nightingale "

I am grateful for...

_____

_____

_____

My big vision or goal I'm working toward:

_____

_____

_____

The thing(s) I will accomplish today to support my vision and goals:

1. _____

2. _____

3. _____

My schedule or action plan:

_____

_____

_____

_____

Thoughts/ideas:

_____

_____

_____

_____

Day 42 Evening Ritual

What great things happened today? What did you get done?

_____

_____

_____

_____

What could've gone better? What lessons did you learn?

_____

_____

_____

_____

What do you want to accomplish tomorrow?

_____

_____

_____

_____

Final notes and ideas:

_____

_____

_____

_____

Day 43 Morning Ritual | Date: _____

 If you work on something a little bit every day, you end up with something that is massive. – Kenneth Goldsmith

I am grateful for...

_____

_____

_____

My big vision or goal I'm working toward:

_____

_____

_____

The thing(s) I will accomplish today to support my vision and goals:

1. _____

2. _____

3. _____

My schedule or action plan:

_____

_____

_____

_____

Thoughts/ideas:

_____

_____

_____

_____

Day 43 Evening Ritual

What great things happened today? What did you get done?

_____

_____

_____

_____

What could've gone better? What lessons did you learn?

_____

_____

_____

_____

What do you want to accomplish tomorrow?

_____

_____

_____

_____

Final notes and ideas:

_____

_____

_____

_____

Day 44 Morning Ritual | Date: _____

> The big secret in life is that there is no secret. Whatever your goal, you can get there if you're willing to work. – Oprah Winfrey

I am grateful for...

_____

_____

_____

My big vision or goal I'm working toward:

_____

_____

_____

The thing(s) I will accomplish today to support my vision and goals:

1. _____

2. _____

3. _____

My schedule or action plan:

_____

_____

_____

_____

Thoughts/ideas:

_____

_____

_____

Day 44 Evening Ritual

What great things happened today? What did you get done?

_____

_____

_____

_____

What could've gone better? What lessons did you learn?

_____

_____

_____

_____

What do you want to accomplish tomorrow?

_____

_____

_____

_____

Final notes and ideas:

_____

_____

_____

_____

Day 45 Morning Ritual | Date: _____

> If you cannot do great things, do small things in a great way. – Napoleon Hill

I am grateful for...

_____

_____

_____

My big vision or goal I'm working toward:

_____

_____

_____

The thing(s) I will accomplish today to support my vision and goals:

1. _____

2. _____

3. _____

My schedule or action plan:

_____

_____

_____

_____

Thoughts/ideas:

_____

_____

_____

Day 45 Evening Ritual

What great things happened today? What did you get done?

_____

_____

_____

_____

What could've gone better? What lessons did you learn?

_____

_____

_____

_____

What do you want to accomplish tomorrow?

_____

_____

_____

_____

Final notes and ideas:

_____

_____

_____

_____

Day 46 Morning Ritual | Date: _____

> Very little is needed to make a happy life; it is all within yourself, in your way of thinking – Marcus Aurelius

I am grateful for...

_____

_____

_____

My big vision or goal I'm working toward:

_____

_____

The thing(s) I will accomplish today to support my vision and goals:

1. _____

2. _____

3. _____

My schedule or action plan:

_____

_____

_____

Thoughts/ideas:

_____

_____

_____

Day 46 Evening Ritual

What great things happened today? What did you get done?

What could've gone better? What lessons did you learn?

What do you want to accomplish tomorrow?

Final notes and ideas:

Day 47 Morning Ritual | Date: _____

> Amateurs sit around and wait for inspiration. The rest of us just get up and go to work. – Stephen King

I am grateful for...

_____
_____
_____

My big vision or goal I'm working toward:

_____
_____

The thing(s) I will accomplish today to support my vision and goals:

1. _____
2. _____
3. _____

My schedule or action plan:

_____
_____
_____

Thoughts/ideas:

_____
_____
_____

Day 47 Evening Ritual

What great things happened today? What did you get done?

What could've gone better? What lessons did you learn?

What do you want to accomplish tomorrow?

Final notes and ideas:

Day 48 Morning Ritual | Date: _____

> Your work is going to fill a large part of your life, and the only way to be truly satisfied is to do what you believe is great work. And the only way to do great work is to love what you do. If you haven't found it yet, keep looking. Don't settle. As with all matters of the heart, you'll know when you find it. – Steve Jobs

I am grateful for...

_____

_____

My big vision or goal I'm working toward:

_____

_____

The thing(s) I will accomplish today to support my vision and goals:

1. _____

2. _____

3. _____

My schedule or action plan:

_____

_____

_____

Thoughts/ideas:

_____

_____

Day 48 Evening Ritual

What great things happened today? What did you get done?

_____

_____

_____

_____

What could've gone better? What lessons did you learn?

_____

_____

_____

_____

What do you want to accomplish tomorrow?

_____

_____

_____

_____

Final notes and ideas:

_____

_____

_____

_____

Day 49 Morning Ritual | Date: _____

> Don't limit your challenges.
> Challenge your limits. – Unknown

I am grateful for...

_____
_____
_____

My big vision or goal I'm working toward:

_____
_____
_____

The thing(s) I will accomplish today to support my vision and goals:

1. _____
2. _____
3. _____

My schedule or action plan:

_____
_____
_____
_____

Thoughts/ideas:

_____
_____
_____

Day 49 Evening Ritual

What great things happened today? What did you get done?

What could've gone better? What lessons did you learn?

What do you want to accomplish tomorrow?

Final notes and ideas:

Day 50 Morning Ritual | Date: _____

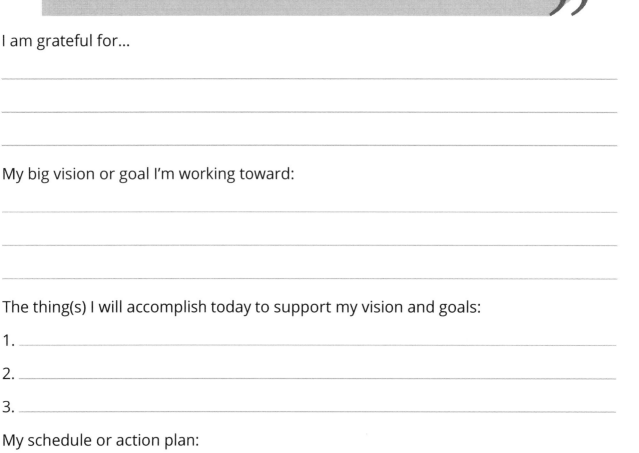

> **Whenever you find yourself doubting how far you can go, just remember how far you have come. – Unknown**

I am grateful for...

_____

_____

_____

My big vision or goal I'm working toward:

_____

_____

The thing(s) I will accomplish today to support my vision and goals:

1. _____

2. _____

3. _____

My schedule or action plan:

_____

_____

_____

Thoughts/ideas:

_____

_____

_____

Day 50 Evening Ritual

What great things happened today? What did you get done?

What could've gone better? What lessons did you learn?

What do you want to accomplish tomorrow?

Final notes and ideas:

Day 51 Morning Ritual | Date: _____

> "Everyone has inside them a piece of good news.
> The good news is you don't know how great you can be!
> How much you can love! What you can accomplish!
> And what your potential is." – Anne Frank

I am grateful for...

_____

_____

_____

My big vision or goal I'm working toward:

_____

_____

_____

The thing(s) I will accomplish today to support my vision and goals:

1. _____

2. _____

3. _____

My schedule or action plan:

_____

_____

_____

_____

Thoughts/ideas:

_____

_____

_____

Day 51 Evening Ritual

What great things happened today? What did you get done?

_____

_____

_____

_____

What could've gone better? What lessons did you learn?

_____

_____

_____

_____

What do you want to accomplish tomorrow?

_____

_____

_____

_____

Final notes and ideas:

_____

_____

_____

_____

Day 52 Morning Ritual | Date: _____

> In the middle of every difficulty lies opportunity. – Albert Einstein

I am grateful for...

_____
_____
_____

My big vision or goal I'm working toward:

_____
_____
_____

The thing(s) I will accomplish today to support my vision and goals:

1. _____
2. _____
3. _____

My schedule or action plan:

_____
_____
_____

Thoughts/ideas:

_____
_____
_____

Day 52 Evening Ritual

What great things happened today? What did you get done?

_____

_____

_____

_____

What could've gone better? What lessons did you learn?

_____

_____

_____

_____

What do you want to accomplish tomorrow?

_____

_____

_____

_____

Final notes and ideas:

_____

_____

_____

_____

Day 53 Morning Ritual | Date: _____

> Start where you are. Use what you have.
> Do what you can. – Arthur Ashe

I am grateful for...

_____

_____

_____

My big vision or goal I'm working toward:

_____

_____

_____

The thing(s) I will accomplish today to support my vision and goals:

1. _____

2. _____

3. _____

My schedule or action plan:

_____

_____

_____

_____

Thoughts/ideas:

_____

_____

_____

Day 53 Evening Ritual

What great things happened today? What did you get done?

What could've gone better? What lessons did you learn?

What do you want to accomplish tomorrow?

Final notes and ideas:

Day 54 Morning Ritual | Date: _____

 Dreams don't work unless you do.
– John C. Maxwell

I am grateful for...

_____
_____
_____

My big vision or goal I'm working toward:

_____
_____

The thing(s) I will accomplish today to support my vision and goals:

1. _____

2. _____

3. _____

My schedule or action plan:

_____
_____
_____

Thoughts/ideas:

_____
_____
_____

Day 54 Evening Ritual

What great things happened today? What did you get done?

_____

_____

_____

_____

What could've gone better? What lessons did you learn?

_____

_____

_____

_____

What do you want to accomplish tomorrow?

_____

_____

_____

_____

Final notes and ideas:

_____

_____

_____

_____

Day 55 Morning Ritual | Date: _____

> Make each day your masterpiece.
> – John Wooden

I am grateful for...

_____
_____
_____

My big vision or goal I'm working toward:

_____
_____
_____

The thing(s) I will accomplish today to support my vision and goals:

1. _____
2. _____
3. _____

My schedule or action plan:

_____
_____
_____
_____

Thoughts/ideas:

_____
_____
_____
_____

Day 55 Evening Ritual

What great things happened today? What did you get done?

What could've gone better? What lessons did you learn?

What do you want to accomplish tomorrow?

Final notes and ideas:

Day 56 Morning Ritual | Date: _____

> Every champion was once a contender that didn't give up. – Gabby Douglas

I am grateful for...

_____
_____
_____

My big vision or goal I'm working toward:

_____
_____
_____

The thing(s) I will accomplish today to support my vision and goals:

1. _____
2. _____
3. _____

My schedule or action plan:

_____
_____
_____
_____

Thoughts/ideas:

_____
_____

_____

Day 56 Evening Ritual

What great things happened today? What did you get done?

What could've gone better? What lessons did you learn?

What do you want to accomplish tomorrow?

Final notes and ideas:

Day 57 Morning Ritual | Date: _____

> Success is liking yourself, liking what you do,
> and liking how you do it. – Maya Angelou

I am grateful for...

_____

_____

_____

My big vision or goal I'm working toward:

_____

_____

_____

The thing(s) I will accomplish today to support my vision and goals:

1. _____

2. _____

3. _____

My schedule or action plan:

_____

_____

_____

Thoughts/ideas:

_____

_____

_____

Day 57 Evening Ritual

What great things happened today? What did you get done?

_____

_____

_____

_____

What could've gone better? What lessons did you learn?

_____

_____

_____

_____

What do you want to accomplish tomorrow?

_____

_____

_____

_____

Final notes and ideas:

_____

_____

_____

_____

Day 58 Morning Ritual | Date: _____

 Doubt kills more dreams than failure ever will. – Suzy Kassem

I am grateful for...

_____

_____

_____

My big vision or goal I'm working toward:

_____

_____

_____

The thing(s) I will accomplish today to support my vision and goals:

1. _____

2. _____

3. _____

My schedule or action plan:

_____

_____

_____

_____

Thoughts/ideas:

_____

_____

 _____

Day 58 Evening Ritual

What great things happened today? What did you get done?

_____

_____

_____

What could've gone better? What lessons did you learn?

_____

_____

_____

What do you want to accomplish tomorrow?

_____

_____

_____

Final notes and ideas:

_____

_____

_____

_____

Day 59 Morning Ritual | Date: _____

 I never lose. Either I win or learn.
– Nelson Mandela

I am grateful for...

_____
_____
_____

My big vision or goal I'm working toward:

_____
_____
_____

The thing(s) I will accomplish today to support my vision and goals:

1. _____
2. _____
3. _____

My schedule or action plan:

_____
_____
_____
_____

Thoughts/ideas:

_____
_____
_____

Day 59 Evening Ritual

What great things happened today? What did you get done?

_____

_____

_____

_____

What could've gone better? What lessons did you learn?

_____

_____

_____

_____

What do you want to accomplish tomorrow?

_____

_____

_____

_____

Final notes and ideas:

_____

_____

_____

_____

Day 60 Morning Ritual | Date: _____

 Today is your opportunity to build the tomorrow you want. – Ken Poirot

I am grateful for...

_____

_____

_____

My big vision or goal I'm working toward:

_____

_____

The thing(s) I will accomplish today to support my vision and goals:

1. _____

2. _____

3. _____

My schedule or action plan:

_____

_____

_____

Thoughts/ideas:

_____

_____

_____

Day 60 Evening Ritual

What great things happened today? What did you get done?

_____

_____

_____

_____

What could've gone better? What lessons did you learn?

_____

_____

_____

_____

What do you want to accomplish tomorrow?

_____

_____

_____

_____

Final notes and ideas:

_____

_____

_____

_____

Day 61 Morning Ritual | Date: _____

 Focus on being productive instead
of busy. – Tim Ferriss

I am grateful for...

_____

_____

_____

My big vision or goal I'm working toward:

_____

_____

_____

The thing(s) I will accomplish today to support my vision and goals:

1. _____

2. _____

3. _____

My schedule or action plan:

_____

_____

_____

_____

Thoughts/ideas:

_____

_____

_____

_____

Day 61 Evening Ritual

What great things happened today? What did you get done?

_____

_____

_____

_____

What could've gone better? What lessons did you learn?

_____

_____

_____

_____

What do you want to accomplish tomorrow?

_____

_____

_____

_____

Final notes and ideas:

_____

_____

_____

_____

Day 62 Morning Ritual | Date: _____

> You don't need to see the whole staircase,
> just take the first step. – Martin Luther King Jr.

I am grateful for...

_____
_____

_____

My big vision or goal I'm working toward:

_____

_____

The thing(s) I will accomplish today to support my vision and goals:

1. _____

2. _____

3. _____

My schedule or action plan:

_____

_____

_____

Thoughts/ideas:

_____

_____

_____

Day 62 Evening Ritual

What great things happened today? What did you get done?

What could've gone better? What lessons did you learn?

What do you want to accomplish tomorrow?

Final notes and ideas:

Day 63 Morning Ritual | Date: _____

 I didn't get there by wishing for it,
but by working for it. – Estee Lauder

I am grateful for...

_____

_____

_____

My big vision or goal I'm working toward:

_____

_____

The thing(s) I will accomplish today to support my vision and goals:

1. _____

2. _____

3. _____

My schedule or action plan:

_____

_____

_____

Thoughts/ideas:

_____

_____

_____

Day 63 Evening Ritual

What great things happened today? What did you get done?

What could've gone better? What lessons did you learn?

What do you want to accomplish tomorrow?

Final notes and ideas:

Day 64 Morning Ritual | Date: _____

> If you're too comfortable, it's time to move on. Terrified of what's next? You're on the right track. – Susan Fales-Hill

I am grateful for...

_____

_____

_____

My big vision or goal I'm working toward:

_____

_____

_____

The thing(s) I will accomplish today to support my vision and goals:

1. _____

2. _____

3. _____

My schedule or action plan:

_____

_____

_____

Thoughts/ideas:

_____

_____

_____

Day 64 Evening Ritual

What great things happened today? What did you get done?

What could've gone better? What lessons did you learn?

What do you want to accomplish tomorrow?

Final notes and ideas:

Day 65 Morning Ritual | Date: _____

 Be happy with what you have while
working for what you want. – Helen Keller

I am grateful for...

_____

_____

_____

My big vision or goal I'm working toward:

_____

_____

_____

The thing(s) I will accomplish today to support my vision and goals:

1. _____

2. _____

3. _____

My schedule or action plan:

_____

_____

_____

_____

Thoughts/ideas:

_____

_____

_____

Day 65 Evening Ritual

What great things happened today? What did you get done?

_____

_____

_____

_____

What could've gone better? What lessons did you learn?

_____

_____

_____

_____

What do you want to accomplish tomorrow?

_____

_____

_____

_____

Final notes and ideas:

_____

_____

_____

_____

Day 66 Morning Ritual | Date: _____

> Do what you can, with what you have, where you are. – Theodore Roosevelt

I am grateful for...

_____

_____

_____

My big vision or goal I'm working toward:

_____

_____

_____

The thing(s) I will accomplish today to support my vision and goals:

1. _____

2. _____

3. _____

My schedule or action plan:

_____

_____

_____

_____

Thoughts/ideas:

_____

_____

_____

_____

Day 66 Evening Ritual

What great things happened today? What did you get done?

_____

_____

_____

_____

What could've gone better? What lessons did you learn?

_____

_____

_____

_____

What do you want to accomplish tomorrow?

_____

_____

_____

_____

Final notes and ideas:

_____

_____

_____

_____

Day 67 Morning Ritual | Date: _____

> If you can dream it, you can do it.
> – Walt Disney

I am grateful for...

_____

_____

_____

My big vision or goal I'm working toward:

_____

_____

_____

The thing(s) I will accomplish today to support my vision and goals:

1. _____

2. _____

3. _____

My schedule or action plan:

_____

_____

_____

_____

Thoughts/ideas:

_____

_____

_____

Day 67 Evening Ritual

What great things happened today? What did you get done?

What could've gone better? What lessons did you learn?

What do you want to accomplish tomorrow?

Final notes and ideas:

Day 68 Morning Ritual | Date: _____

 You can do anything you set your mind to.
– Benjamin Franklin

I am grateful for...

_____

_____

_____

My big vision or goal I'm working toward:

_____

_____

The thing(s) I will accomplish today to support my vision and goals:

1. _____

2. _____

3. _____

My schedule or action plan:

_____

_____

_____

Thoughts/ideas:

_____

_____

_____

Day 68 Evening Ritual

What great things happened today? What did you get done?

What could've gone better? What lessons did you learn?

What do you want to accomplish tomorrow?

Final notes and ideas:

Day 69 Morning Ritual | Date: _____

 Twenty years from now you'll be more disappointed by the things you did not do than the ones you did. – Mark Twain

I am grateful for...

_____

_____

_____

My big vision or goal I'm working toward:

_____

_____

_____

The thing(s) I will accomplish today to support my vision and goals:

1. _____

2. _____

3. _____

My schedule or action plan:

_____

_____

_____

Thoughts/ideas:

_____

_____

_____

Day 69 Evening Ritual

What great things happened today? What did you get done?

_____

_____

_____

_____

What could've gone better? What lessons did you learn?

_____

_____

_____

_____

What do you want to accomplish tomorrow?

_____

_____

_____

_____

Final notes and ideas:

_____

_____

_____

_____

_____

Day 70 Morning Ritual | Date: _____

> " A winner is a dreamer who never gives up.
> – Nelson Mandela "

I am grateful for...

_____
_____
_____

My big vision or goal I'm working toward:

_____
_____

The thing(s) I will accomplish today to support my vision and goals:

1. _____

2. _____

3. _____

My schedule or action plan:

_____
_____
_____

Thoughts/ideas:

_____
_____
_____

Day 70 Evening Ritual

What great things happened today? What did you get done?

_____

_____

_____

_____

What could've gone better? What lessons did you learn?

_____

_____

_____

_____

What do you want to accomplish tomorrow?

_____

_____

_____

_____

Final notes and ideas:

_____

_____

_____

_____

_____

Day 71 Morning Ritual | Date: _____

 If you are not willing to risk the usual you will have to settle for the ordinary. – Jim Rohn

I am grateful for...

_____

_____

_____

My big vision or goal I'm working toward:

_____

_____

The thing(s) I will accomplish today to support my vision and goals:

1. _____

2. _____

3. _____

My schedule or action plan:

_____

_____

_____

Thoughts/ideas:

_____

_____

_____

Day 71 Evening Ritual

What great things happened today? What did you get done?

What could've gone better? What lessons did you learn?

What do you want to accomplish tomorrow?

Final notes and ideas:

Day 72 Morning Ritual | Date: _____

 Success is walking from failure to failure with no loss of enthusiasm. – Winston Churchill

I am grateful for...

_____

_____

My big vision or goal I'm working toward:

_____

_____

The thing(s) I will accomplish today to support my vision and goals:

1. _____

2. _____

3. _____

My schedule or action plan:

_____

_____

_____

Thoughts/ideas:

_____

_____

_____

Day 72 Evening Ritual

What great things happened today? What did you get done?

_____

_____

_____

_____

What could've gone better? What lessons did you learn?

_____

_____

_____

_____

What do you want to accomplish tomorrow?

_____

_____

_____

_____

Final notes and ideas:

_____

_____

_____

_____

_____

Day 73 Morning Ritual | Date: _____

> " I believe that the only courage anybody ever needs is the courage to follow your own dreams. – Oprah Winfrey "

I am grateful for...

_____
_____
_____

My big vision or goal I'm working toward:

_____
_____
_____

The thing(s) I will accomplish today to support my vision and goals:

1. _____
2. _____
3. _____

My schedule or action plan:

_____
_____
_____
_____

Thoughts/ideas:

_____
_____
_____

Day 73 Evening Ritual

What great things happened today? What did you get done?

_____

_____

_____

_____

What could've gone better? What lessons did you learn?

_____

_____

_____

_____

What do you want to accomplish tomorrow?

_____

_____

_____

_____

Final notes and ideas:

_____

_____

_____

_____

Day 74 Morning Ritual | Date: _____

 The starting point of all achievement is desire. – Napoleon Hill

I am grateful for...

_____
_____

_____

My big vision or goal I'm working toward:

_____

_____

The thing(s) I will accomplish today to support my vision and goals:

1. _____

2. _____

3. _____

My schedule or action plan:

_____

_____

_____

Thoughts/ideas:

_____

_____

_____

Day 74 Evening Ritual

What great things happened today? What did you get done?

_____

_____

_____

_____

What could've gone better? What lessons did you learn?

_____

_____

_____

_____

What do you want to accomplish tomorrow?

_____

_____

_____

_____

Final notes and ideas:

_____

_____

_____

_____

_____

Day 75 Morning Ritual | Date: _____

 Courage is resistance to fear, mastery of fear–not absence of fear. – Mark Twain

I am grateful for...

My big vision or goal I'm working toward:

The thing(s) I will accomplish today to support my vision and goals:

1. _____

2. _____

3. _____

My schedule or action plan:

Thoughts/ideas:

Day 75 Evening Ritual

What great things happened today? What did you get done?

_____

_____

_____

_____

What could've gone better? What lessons did you learn?

_____

_____

_____

_____

What do you want to accomplish tomorrow?

_____

_____

_____

_____

Final notes and ideas:

_____

_____

_____

_____

Day 76 Morning Ritual | Date: _____

> Only put off until tomorrow what you are willing to die having left undone. – Pablo Picasso

I am grateful for...

_____
_____
_____

My big vision or goal I'm working toward:

_____
_____
_____

The thing(s) I will accomplish today to support my vision and goals:

1. _____
2. _____
3. _____

My schedule or action plan:

_____
_____
_____
_____

Thoughts/ideas:

_____
_____
_____
_____

Day 76 Evening Ritual

What great things happened today? What did you get done?

_____

_____

_____

_____

What could've gone better? What lessons did you learn?

_____

_____

_____

_____

What do you want to accomplish tomorrow?

_____

_____

_____

_____

Final notes and ideas:

_____

_____

_____

_____

Day 77 Morning Ritual | Date: _____

 People often say that motivation doesn't last. Well, neither does bathing–that's why we recommend it daily. – Zig Ziglar

I am grateful for...

_____

_____

_____

My big vision or goal I'm working toward:

_____

_____

_____

The thing(s) I will accomplish today to support my vision and goals:

1. _____

2. _____

3. _____

My schedule or action plan:

_____

_____

_____

_____

Thoughts/ideas:

_____

_____

 _____

_____

Day 77 Evening Ritual

What great things happened today? What did you get done?

_____

_____

_____

_____

What could've gone better? What lessons did you learn?

_____

_____

_____

_____

What do you want to accomplish tomorrow?

_____

_____

_____

_____

Final notes and ideas:

_____

_____

_____

_____

Day 78 Morning Ritual | Date: _____

 The only place where success comes before work is in the dictionary. – Vidal Sassoon

I am grateful for...

_____
_____
_____

My big vision or goal I'm working toward:

_____
_____
_____

The thing(s) I will accomplish today to support my vision and goals:

1. _____

2. _____

3. _____

My schedule or action plan:

_____
_____
_____

Thoughts/ideas:

_____
_____
_____

Day 78 Evening Ritual

What great things happened today? What did you get done?

What could've gone better? What lessons did you learn?

What do you want to accomplish tomorrow?

Final notes and ideas:

Day 79 Morning Ritual | Date: _____

 Too many of us are not living our dreams because we are living our fears. – Les Brown

I am grateful for...

_____
_____
_____

My big vision or goal I'm working toward:

_____
_____

The thing(s) I will accomplish today to support my vision and goals:

1. _____
2. _____
3. _____

My schedule or action plan:

_____
_____
_____

Thoughts/ideas:

_____
_____
_____

Day 79 Evening Ritual

What great things happened today? What did you get done?

_____

_____

_____

_____

What could've gone better? What lessons did you learn?

_____

_____

_____

_____

What do you want to accomplish tomorrow?

_____

_____

_____

_____

Final notes and ideas:

_____

_____

_____

_____

_____

Day 80 Morning Ritual | Date: _____

 It's what you practice in private that you will be rewarded for in public. – Tony Robbins

I am grateful for...

_____

_____

_____

My big vision or goal I'm working toward:

_____

_____

The thing(s) I will accomplish today to support my vision and goals:

1. _____

2. _____

3. _____

My schedule or action plan:

_____

_____

_____

Thoughts/ideas:

_____

_____

_____

Day 80 Evening Ritual

What great things happened today? What did you get done?

_____

_____

_____

_____

What could've gone better? What lessons did you learn?

_____

_____

_____

_____

What do you want to accomplish tomorrow?

_____

_____

_____

_____

Final notes and ideas:

_____

_____

_____

_____

Day 81 Morning Ritual | Date: _____

> When it comes down to it, nothing trumps execution. – Gary Vaynerchuk

I am grateful for...

_____
_____
_____

My big vision or goal I'm working toward:

_____
_____
_____

The thing(s) I will accomplish today to support my vision and goals:

1. _____
2. _____
3. _____

My schedule or action plan:

_____
_____
_____

Thoughts/ideas:

_____
_____
_____

Day 81 Evening Ritual

What great things happened today? What did you get done?

_____

_____

_____

_____

What could've gone better? What lessons did you learn?

_____

_____

_____

_____

What do you want to accomplish tomorrow?

_____

_____

_____

_____

Final notes and ideas:

_____

_____

_____

_____

_____

Day 82 Morning Ritual | Date: _____

> *Whether you think you can, or you think you can't–you're right. – Henry Ford*

I am grateful for...

_____

_____

My big vision or goal I'm working toward:

_____

_____

The thing(s) I will accomplish today to support my vision and goals:

1. _____

2. _____

3. _____

My schedule or action plan:

_____

_____

_____

Thoughts/ideas:

_____

_____

_____

Day 82 Evening Ritual

What great things happened today? What did you get done?

What could've gone better? What lessons did you learn?

What do you want to accomplish tomorrow?

Final notes and ideas:

Day 83 Morning Ritual | Date: _____

> Find out what you like doing best, and get someone to pay you for doing it. – Kathereine Whitehorn

I am grateful for...

_____

_____

_____

My big vision or goal I'm working toward:

_____

_____

The thing(s) I will accomplish today to support my vision and goals:

1. _____

2. _____

3. _____

My schedule or action plan:

_____

_____

_____

Thoughts/ideas:

_____

_____

_____

Day 83 Evening Ritual

What great things happened today? What did you get done?

What could've gone better? What lessons did you learn?

What do you want to accomplish tomorrow?

Final notes and ideas:

Day 84 Morning Ritual | Date: _____

 If you do what you've always done, you'll get what you've always gotten. – Tony Robbins

I am grateful for...

_____

_____

_____

My big vision or goal I'm working toward:

_____

_____

_____

The thing(s) I will accomplish today to support my vision and goals:

1. _____

2. _____

3. _____

My schedule or action plan:

_____

_____

_____

_____

Thoughts/ideas:

_____

_____

_____

_____

Day 84 Evening Ritual

What great things happened today? What did you get done?

_____

_____

_____

_____

What could've gone better? What lessons did you learn?

_____

_____

_____

_____

What do you want to accomplish tomorrow?

_____

_____

_____

_____

Final notes and ideas:

_____

_____

_____

_____

Day 85 Morning Ritual | Date: _____

 If opportunity doesn't knock, build a door.
– Milton Berle

I am grateful for...

_____

_____

_____

My big vision or goal I'm working toward:

_____

_____

_____

The thing(s) I will accomplish today to support my vision and goals:

1. _____

2. _____

3. _____

My schedule or action plan:

_____

_____

_____

Thoughts/ideas:

_____

_____

_____

Day 85 Evening Ritual

What great things happened today? What did you get done?

_____

_____

_____

_____

What could've gone better? What lessons did you learn?

_____

_____

_____

_____

What do you want to accomplish tomorrow?

_____

_____

_____

_____

Final notes and ideas:

_____

_____

_____

_____

Day 86 Morning Ritual | Date: _____

 The future depends on what you do today.
– Mahatma Gandhi

I am grateful for...

_____
_____

My big vision or goal I'm working toward:

_____
_____

The thing(s) I will accomplish today to support my vision and goals:

1. _____
2. _____
3. _____

My schedule or action plan:

_____
_____
_____

Thoughts/ideas:

_____
_____
_____

Day 86 Evening Ritual

What great things happened today? What did you get done?

_____

_____

_____

_____

What could've gone better? What lessons did you learn?

_____

_____

_____

_____

What do you want to accomplish tomorrow?

_____

_____

_____

Final notes and ideas:

_____

_____

_____

_____

Day 87 Morning Ritual | Date: _____

 I am not a product of my circumstances. I am a product of my decisions. – Stephen Covey

I am grateful for...

_____
_____
_____

My big vision or goal I'm working toward:

_____
_____
_____

The thing(s) I will accomplish today to support my vision and goals:

1. _____
2. _____
3. _____

My schedule or action plan:

_____
_____
_____

Thoughts/ideas:

_____
_____
_____

Day 87 Evening Ritual

What great things happened today? What did you get done?

What could've gone better? What lessons did you learn?

What do you want to accomplish tomorrow?

Final notes and ideas:

Day 88 Morning Ritual | Date: _____

> Failure is only the opportunity more intelligently to begin again. – Henry Ford

I am grateful for...

_____

_____

_____

My big vision or goal I'm working toward:

_____

_____

The thing(s) I will accomplish today to support my vision and goals:

1. _____

2. _____

3. _____

My schedule or action plan:

_____

_____

_____

Thoughts/ideas:

_____

_____

_____

Day 88 Evening Ritual

What great things happened today? What did you get done?

What could've gone better? What lessons did you learn?

What do you want to accomplish tomorrow?

Final notes and ideas:

Day 89 Morning Ritual | Date: _____

> The meeting of preparation with opportunity generates the offspring we call luck. – Tony Robbins

I am grateful for...

_____

_____

_____

My big vision or goal I'm working toward:

_____

_____

_____

The thing(s) I will accomplish today to support my vision and goals:

1. _____

2. _____

3. _____

My schedule or action plan:

_____

_____

_____

Thoughts/ideas:

_____

_____

_____

Day 89 Evening Ritual

What great things happened today? What did you get done?

_____

_____

_____

_____

What could've gone better? What lessons did you learn?

_____

_____

_____

_____

What do you want to accomplish tomorrow?

_____

_____

_____

_____

Final notes and ideas:

_____

_____

_____

_____

Day 90 Morning Ritual | Date: _____

> Love the life you have while you create the life
> of your dreams. Don't think you have to choose
> one over the other. – Hal Elrod

I am grateful for...

_____
_____
_____

My big vision or goal I'm working toward:

_____
_____

The thing(s) I will accomplish today to support my vision and goals:

1. _____

2. _____

3. _____

My schedule or action plan:

_____
_____
_____
_____

Thoughts/ideas:

_____
_____
_____
_____

Day 90 Evening Ritual

What great things happened today? What did you get done?

What could've gone better? What lessons did you learn?

What do you want to accomplish tomorrow?

Final notes and ideas:

Reflection Time

Congratulations on finishing the journal! Please take some time for reflection and answer these questions:

What were your biggest accomplishments over the last 90 days?

_____

_____

_____

What were your biggest mistakes and lessons learned?

_____

_____

_____

What habits were helpful?

_____

_____

_____

What habits do you want to continue or establish in the future?

_____

_____

_____

What will your next 90-day goal be?

_____

_____

_____

Notes

Notes

Notes

Notes

Notes

Notes and Ideas

Notes and Ideas

Notes and Ideas

Notes and Ideas

Notes and Ideas

Thanks for using the *Own Your Career Own Your Life* Journal. You can grab the book and your next journal on Amazon or at ownyourcareerownyourlife.com.

And please come share your goals and accomplishments in our Facebook group. Ownyourcareerownyourlife.com/facebook

You can order your next journal on Amazon.

Made in the USA
Columbia, SC
29 November 2020